TWELFTH NIGHT

William Shakespeare

LAKE Illustrated CLASSICS

LAKE EDUCATION
Belmont, California

LAKE ILLUSTRATED CLASSICS

Collection 1

Black Beauty, The Call of the Wild, Dr. Jekyll and Mr. Hyde, Dracula, Frankenstein, Huckleberry Finn, Moby Dick, The Red Badge of Courage, The Time Machine, Tom Sawyer, Treasure Island, 20,000 Leagues Under the Sea

Collection 2

The Great Adventures of Sherlock Holmes, Gulliver's Travels, The Hunchback of Notre Dame, The Invisible Man, Journey to the Center of the Earth, Kidnapped, The Mysterious Island, The Scarlet Letter, The Story of My Life, A Tale of Two Cities, The Three Musketeers, The War of the Worlds

Collection 3

Around the World in Eighty Days, Captains Courageous, A Connecticut Yankee in King Arthur's Court, The Hound of the Baskervilles, The House of the Seven Gables, Jany Eyre, The Last of the Mohicans, The Best of O. Henry, The Best of Poe, Two Years Before the Mast, White Fang, Wuthering Heights

Collection 4

Ben Hur, A Christmas Carol, The Food of the Gods, Ivanhoe, The Man in the Iron Mask, The Prince and the Pauper, The Prisoner of Zenda, The Return of the Native, Robinson Crusoe, The Scarlet Pimpernel, The Sea Wolf, The Swiss Family Robinson

Collection 5

Billy Budd, Crime and Punishment, Don Quixote, Great Expectations, Heidi, The Iliad, Lord Jim, The Mutiny on Board H.M.S. Bounty, The Odyssey, Oliver Twist, Pride and Prejudice, The Turn of the Screw

Shakespeare Collection

As You Like It, Hamlet, Julius Caesar, King Lear, Macbeth, The Merchant of Venice, A Midsummer Night's Dream, Othello, Romeo and Juliet, The Taming of the Shrew, The Tempest, Twelfth Night

ISBN 1-56103-688-9

Printed in the United States of America

1 9 8 7 6 5 4 3 2

to the reader

Welcome to the **LAKE ILLUSTRATED SHAKESPEARE** series!

You are about to enjoy a dramatic story that people have been enjoying for almost 400 years. With the help of pictures as well as words, you can find out for yourself why Shakespeare is known as the greatest playwright in the English language. With **Lake Illustrated Shakespeare**, now you can *see* Shakespeare's greatest characters as you read about them!

In Shakespeare's day, people enjoyed going to the theater for the same reasons that people today enjoy theater or movies or TV. They liked Shakespeare's colorful characters, whether they were heroes or villains. They liked the action, the humor, and the suspense. They liked story plots that dealt with great human themes, such as ambition and jealousy, love and revenge. In other words, the people in Shakespeare's day liked the same story elements that we do.

The plays of William Shakespeare provide all of these elements and more to readers of any time and place.

Someday you may want to read the plays in their original form. When you do, you will discover the richness of language that makes Shakespeare Shakespeare. In the meantime, sit back and prepare yourself for a great reading experience. We guarantee you'll be caught up in the action before you know it.

—The Editors

about the author

William Shakespeare was born on April 23, 1564, in Stratford-on-Avon, England, the third child of John Shakespeare, a well-to-do merchant, and Mary Arden, his wife. Young William probably attended the Stratford grammar school, where he learned English, Greek, and a great deal of Latin.

In 1582 Shakespeare married Anne Hathaway. By 1583 the couple had a daughter, Susánna, and two years later the twins, Hamnet and Judith. Somewhere between 1585 and 1592 Shakespeare went to London, where he became first an actor and then a playwright. His acting company, The King's Men, appeared most often in the Globe theatre, a part of which Shakespeare himself owned.

In all, Shakespeare is believed to have written thirty-seven plays, several nondramatic poems, and a number of sonnets. In 1611 when he left the active life of the theatre, he returned to Stratford and became a country gentleman, living in the second-largest house in town. For five years he lived a quiet life. Then, on April 23, 1616, William Shakespeare died and was buried in Trinity Church in Stratford. From his own time to the present, Shakespeare is considered one of the greatest writers of the English-speaking world.

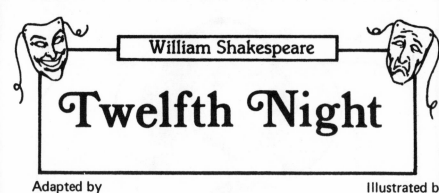

William Shakespeare

Twelfth Night

Adapted by
NAUNERLE FARR

Illustrated by
E.R. CRUZ

a
VINCENT FAGO
production

Viola
Sebastian
Orsino
Olivia

Many years ago, Orsino, Duke* of Illyria, sat in his palace thinking of Olivia, the woman he loved.
If music is the food of love, play on. If I am fed too much, maybe I'll lose my appetite** for both.
But Olivia was not interested in the duke. Her brother had just died, and she had decided to do nothing but weep for him.

*a noble title
**desire for food

As he was speaking, one of his servants entered the room.
Did you see Olivia? What is the news?
Sir, she would not see me, but I spoke to her maid.
Lady Olivia says that for seven years not even the skies shall see her face! She will always appear wearing a veil like a nun.
Every day she will weep for her brother and spend her time thinking of him.
What a heart she has! Think of how much she will love when Cupid's* arrow strikes her.

*the god of love

eanwhile, many miles from the
uke's palace, a storm was raging
n the sea. A great ship has just
one down, and the people were
orced to swim for shore.
The captain, some sailors, and a noble young lady named Viola arrived safely.
We've made it! Are you all right?
Yes . . . I think so.
But Sebastian . . . my twin brother . . . where is he?
We've never been apart! If he has drowned, I don't want to live.
Come, now . . . there's still hope.

We were lucky . . . maybe he will be too. The last I saw of him . . .
Yes, yes?
. . . he had roped himself to a mast,* and it was floating. He may come ashore somewhere, as we did.
Oh, I hope so!
But where are we? Do you know this country?
Yes, madam; it is Illyria. I grew up not three hours' travel from here!
Who rules it?
A noble duke named Orsino

*one of the large poles to which a ship's sails were fastened

Orsino! I've heard my father speak of him. Is he married?
No, but he is much in love with the countess* Olivia. And she. . . .
Yes?
Her brother has lately died. And for love of him, she'll not see or talk to any other man.
Oh, yes! I know how she feels! If only I could stay with her . . . work for her. . . .

*noble lady's title

But she will see no one, listen to no one— not even the duke!
Then I have another idea.
You must find clothes for me like my brother's—and present me to the duke as a boy, to serve him as a page.*
Do this for me, and I will pay you well.
I'll do it.

*a personal servant

While Viola was making her plans, things were busy at Lady Olivia's house. Her uncle, Sir Toby Belch, was complaining* to Maria, the maid.
What does Olivia mean, taking her brother's death this way? I don't like it!
And she doesn't like the late hours you keep and the drinking you do!
She may object as much as she likes, but I'll do as I please.
She does object!
She spoke of it yesterday. And of a foolish man you brought to court** her.
Sir Andrew Aguecheek? He's as tall as any man in Illyria!
And what does that matter?
Well, he also has a lot of money!

*grumbling
**try to win someone's love

He speaks several languages.
He also picks fights. If he were not a coward too, he'd have been challenged* and killed long ago!

And they say he's drunk every night—with *you*!
Only by drinking to my niece's** health. Anyone's a coward who won't drink to my niece!

Here's Sir Andrew now!
Good day, Sir Toby Belch. Good day, fair maid.
And you, too, sir.

*dared to fight
**the daughter of one's sister or brother

I think I'll go home tomorrow, Sir Toby. Your niece won't let me see her.
No, no! Stay awhile.
No, I don't think she'll ever accept *me.* I hear that Duke Orsino is courting her.
But she won't accept him! She says she won't marry anyone higher than herself in title, years, or brains!
Then I'll stay a month longer. We'll have a good time, and I'll dance every night!
Good! We were born to dance!

Meanwhile, at the duke's palace, Viola had become a page. Everyone thought she was a boy, and they called her Cesario.
You've been here only three days, and already you are a favorite of the duke's. You will go far!
Thank you. Here he comes.

Ah, Cesario! I was looking for you.
I am here, sir.

Come, I want to talk to you. The rest of you may leave.

I have told you the secrets of my heart, Cesario. You know of my love for Olivia.
Yes, sir.

You must go and tell her how I love her!
But she will never let me in.

Yes, you're the very one! You are so young and sweet and gentle . . . almost like a girl.

Stay until she sees you. Tell her how faithful* I am.
I'll do my best to win your lady for you.

ue, never-changing

Do well in this, and you may call my fortune your own!
Thank you, sir.
But it will be hard to win her the duke, when I, myself, give anything to be his wife!
For in this short time, Viola fallen deeply in love with Orsino.
But while Viola, dressed as Cesario, was on her way to Olivia's house, Olivia herself was speaking with the fool,* Feste, and the steward,** Malvolio.
I am surprised that a fool like this pleases you, my lady. You could easily find a funnier one!
You wish you could be like him, Malvolio, that is all.
Thank you, dam, for ing well of

*a witty, clown-like entertainer

**a servant who manages the household for his employer

Just then the maid, Maria, entered with a message.
A young man at the gate wishes to speak with you, madam.
Is he from Duke Orsino?
I don't know, but he is very handsome.
Malvolio, go and find out.
If he is from the duke, tell him I am sick, or not at home. Tell him anything, but get rid of him.

Soon Malvolio returned.
Madam, the young man says he must speak with you!
Well, he shall *not*.

He says he'll stand at your door forever until you see him!
What kind of man is he?

He's not old enough to be a man, and not young enough to be a boy. He is very handsome.
Oh, well, let him come in.

Give me my veil. We'll hear once more what message Orsino sends.

Soon "Cesario" came in and spoke to the two women.
The lady of the house . . . which is she?
I will speak for her. What do you wish?

Please tell me if you are Lady Olivia. I don't want to waste my speech!

It is beautifully written, and I've taken great pains to learn it by heart!
Very well, I am Lady Olivia. Tell me what you have to say.

It comes from Orsino's very heart. But please let me see your face!
Very well.
I will pull aside the curtain and show you the picture. Is it well done?
Very well done! Very beautiful! No wonder my master loves you.
But his love for you is so great that it couldn't be repaid even if you were the most beautiful woman in the world!
He is a great and noble man, but he knows how I feel. I cannot love him.
If I loved you as he does, I would not understand that either.

Well, what would *you* do?
I would camp at your gate. I would write love songs and sing them to you day and night.
You would have no rest until you took pity on me.
Tell me, what is your back-ground?
I am a gentle-man. My rank* is higher than my job with Duke Orsino.
I cannot love him. Tell him to send no more messengers . . .
. . . unless, of course, you would come back to tell me how he takes it.
Then good-bye, my lady.

*place in society

With this, Cesario left, and the lady Olivia sat alone.
A gentleman, Cesario? Of course you are! And all of a sudden I am in love with you!
Malvolio, come here!
Run after the duke's messenger. Give him this ring he left behind.
If the young man will come again tomorrow, I'll tell him my reasons. Hurry, Malvolio!
Madam, I am on my way.

And while all this was happening, Viola's twin brother Sebastian had been rescued from drowning by a sea captain named Antonio.
Easy, men . . . steady!

When Sebastian had rested, the two men talked together.
My only family was a dear twin sister. I think she must have drowned some hours before you pulled me from the sea.
I am very sorry.

Sebastian and Antonio quickly became friends. But when the ship docked at Illyria, Sebastian decided to remain ashore.
Aren't you coming back to the ship?
No. I think I will go to Duke Orsino's palace
I would go with you, but I have many enemies there.
Then farewell, good Antonio!

Without knowing it, Sebastian was making his way toward his sister. And she, meanwhile, was being followed by Malvolio.
Wait! Were you not just now with Countess Olivia
Yes, what of it?

She wanted me to return this ring to you. You could have saved me the trouble by tak-ing it away yourself.
You must tell Orsino that she won't have anything to do with him. And you must not return either, unless you can tell her how he takes this news.
She took the ring from me. I won't have it back!
Come, sir, you threw it to her! And she wishes it returned!
There it is, if you think it's worth stooping* for. If not, let it be find-ers keepers!

ending down

What does this mean? I left no ring with her. Duke Orsino sent none.
She thinks that I am a young man. Could she have fallen in love with me?
I suppose she could! Poor lady . . . she'd do better to love a dream!
Duke Orsino loves her dearly; I love him; and she loves me! How can I eve untangle* *this*?

*straighten out; fix

Not knowing any of these things, Sir Toby and Sir Andrew sat up late that night, drinking and enjoying themselves.
Welcome, fool! Come, let's have a song.
Yes, a song! I'll give you six-pence.*
I'll sing you a love song!
"O mistress mine, where are you roaming? O stay and hear! Your true love's coming."
Good! Good!
Just then the maid Maria came into the room.
What awful noise! Lady Olivia will call up Malvolio and have him throw you both out.
Never, never! We're too smart for that!

*a small amount of money; a tip

"On the twelfth day of December. . . ."
For heavens' sake, quiet!
Gentlemen, are you *crazy*? Don't you have anything better to do?
Have you no respect for place, people, or time?
We *did* keep time, sir, in our songs.
My lady says, Sir Toby, that you are welcome here only if you correct your manners! Otherwise, please leave!
"Farewell, dear heart, since I must leave!"
Don't go, Sir Toby!

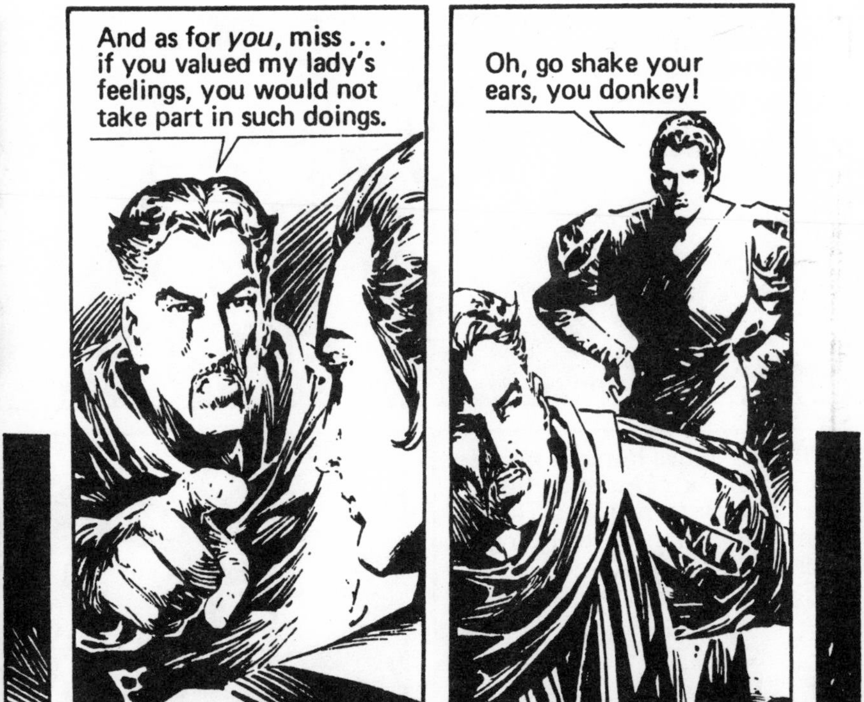
And as for *you*, miss . . . if you valued my lady's feelings, you would not take part in such doings.
Oh, go shake your ears, you donkey!
I'll challenge him to fight. Then I'll make a fool of him!
Do it, Sir Andrew!
Wait, Sir Toby. Leave Malvolio to me. I know how to make a fool of him.

He thinks he is so wonderful that everyone must love him. That's what I'll work on.
What will you do?

I'll drop a love letter in his way. It will speak of his eyes, his walk, the way he looks. He'll know the letter is describing* him.

My writing is very much like Lady Olivia's. We can hardly tell them apart.
And he will think the letter comes from her, and that she's in love with him!

That's it. And I will hide you two where you can watch him. For now, go to bed and dream of it!
You are a good girl, Maria!

*talking about

Good night.
Shall we go?
It's too late now. Let's have another drink!
uring the next ew days, Duke rsino con- inued to dream f Countess livia.
Come away, come away, death, nd in sad cypress* let me be laid. ly away, fly away, breath; am killed by a cruel maid."
That's my favorite song! It's so sad!
f you're ever in love, Cesario, you'll also ike such music.
I do, sir. I know!

coffin made of black cypress wood

What . . . you *are* in love! What sort of woman is she?
She's . . . somewha like you, sir!
She has your coloring . . . she's about your age. . . .
That's wron my boy! Th man should be older tha the woman.
But now you must go back to Olivia. Tell her I don't want her lands or her fortune . . . only herself!
But if she can't love you, what will you do
I won't take that answer!
But perhaps you must! Suppose lady loved you much as you lov Olivia.

Suppose you cannot
love her. You tell
her so. Must she
not accept your
answer?
No woman's heart can hold such love as mine! Don't compare a woman's love for me with mine for Olivia!
My father had a
daughter who loved
man . . . as perhaps
might love you if
were a woman.
What happened?
She never told the man about her love, but faded away from grief,* trying to smile.
But did your sister die of this love?
I am all the daughters of my father, and all the brothers, too.** But I can't answer your question.

dness

ola, who still thinks her brother is dead, means that she is the only child left in her family

Now shall I go to your lady?
Yes, quickly Say again th I won't take "no" for an answer.
Meanwhile, in Countess Olivia's garden, Maria was ready to work out her plan against Malvolio.
He's coming! Quick, hide behind this hedge where you can watch. And keep quiet!
And here's the bait to catch a fo
I would make a goo husband for Olivia! Great ladies *have* been known to marry their steward and Maria says the countess likes me!

Then I would be *Count* Malvolio! And I would say to Sir Toby, "Stop your drunken behavior,* or leave our house!"
How dare he talk that way about me?
Shhhhh!
What's this?
It's Olivia's handwriting! "To my beloved, my good wishes."
"My place is above you, but you can become great. I will help you."
"You must smile when you are near me, and wear the yellow stockings and cross-garters** I like so much."

*way of acting
*items of men's clothing

It is certain that she loves me . . . even if my name is not written here!
I'll go at once and do everything she says!
I could marry Maria for such a clever joke!
Soon after Malvolio had gone, Maria returned.
It worked, my girl!
Good! Lady Olivia hates yellow . . . as well as men who wear cross-garters. And she is too sad to want smiling faces around her. Come and watch what happens.

But before Sir Toby and Sir Andrew could watch Malvolio make a fool of himself, Cesario returned.
Most beautiful lady, may the heavens rain perfume on you!
I am glad you're here. Let everyone leave us.
That young man is too handsome and speaks too well! Olivia likes him!

When they were alone, Cesario tried to talk of Orsino's love. But Olivia would not listen.
No, no! It is only you I love, Cesario . . . no matter what you think of me for telling you!
Well, then, I am sorry for you.

Oh, Cesario, I swear by the flowers of spring . . . by everything good . . . I love you!
And I cannot love you. Yet no woman shall be mistress* of my heart but me! Goodbye, Lady Olivia.
And with that, Cesario returned to the duke's palace.

*owner, boss

Meanwhile, inside Olivia's house . . .
I'm going home! Your niece was nicer to the duke's servant than she ever is to me.
Come, now. Perhaps she did it to make you jealous!*
Why don't you have a duel** with Cesario? Then Olivia will see how brave you are!
He looks too young and gentle to be much of a fighter. I'll do it!
I'll write him a letter and dare him to fight. But you must give it to him for me.
Write it in a strong-looking way. Really scare him!
Just then Maria entered the room.
If you want a good laugh, come with me. Malvolio is on his way to see Olivia.

*wanting what someone else has

**a fight between two people, usually with swords or pistols

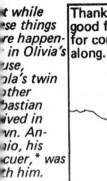

t while
ese things
re happen-
in Olivia's
use,
ola's twin
other
bastian
ived in
wn. An-
nio, his
cuer, was*
th him.

Thank you, good friend, for coming along.
There may be danger for me from the duke's officers. But there is more danger for you, as a stranger, without someone to show you around.

I want to keep out of sight. Shall we find a place to stay?
I would like to look around town first.

Why don't you go by yourself? Take my money in case you want to buy something.

I'll get rooms for us at the Elephant Inn and will meet you there.
Thank you, good Antonio! I will see you in an hour.

omeone who saves another person

On the other side of town, Olivia had just decided to send for Malvolio.
Tell Malvolio to come here. He is serious,* as I am right now.
He is coming, but I think he is crazy! He does nothing but smile!
Ho, ho, ho, sweet lady!
This is a sad time! Why are you acting like this?
I'm wearing yello
stockings and criss
crossed garters—
everything to pleas
you!
You are i
I'm not ill, my lady. I'm just doing what you asked in your letter!
Letter? What letter? He *is* mad! Get my cousin Toby and take good care of him.
Yes,
madan

*not happy or laughing

Soon Sir Toby and a servant came for Malvolio.
Poor man! Be gentle with him.
We will shut him in a dark room where he can't hurt himself.
Go hang your-selves! You are foolish people and not my equals! Let me go!

leanwhile, Sir Andrew finished vriting to Cesario and brought is letter to Sir Toby.
Iere it is . . . ery war-like nd strong. Will ou bring it to he boy now?
He's with my niece. I'll bring it to him, but you stay here and wait until he passes by.

At that moment Cesario was just leaving Olivia's house.
Good sir, you have made a friend of mine very angry! He wants to fight you with his sword.
There must be a mistake! I've hurt no one.

Sir Toby had decided to have some fun by making Sir Andrew and Cesario each frightened of the other.
If you value your life, be on your guard! This man is a fearful fighter!
But I am fighter! I will ask th countess help.
No, you will wait here! Fabian, guard this gentleman until I return with Sir Andrew!
This is ver strange!
Sir Toby found Sir Andrew nearby.
Come on. This lad's a devil! I've never seen such a fighter!
Then I don't want to fight him! How can I get out of it?
You're in for it now! Just draw your sword and do your best. Maybe he'll fee sorry for you!

Soon the two fighters met.
Oh, no! Should I tell them I'm really a woman?
Come! He says he won't hurt you!
Heaven defend me!

The two fighters began their duel. But just then Antonio arrived, looking for Sebastian. Confused,* Antonio thought Viola was her brother.
Stop! Whatever this young man has done, I will defend him!
Thank goodness!
Who are you?

*mixed up

At that moment the duke's officers came by. They had recognized* Antonio on the street.
Antonio, I arrest you on Duke Orsino's orders.
Very well. I see you know who I am and remem ber me.
I was looking for you. Now I must ask you for my money.
Your money, sir? I am very grateful for your help, but I haven't much money.
Here is half of all I have.
You pretend you don't know me? After all I've done for you?
I saved this lad from death in the sea . . . did everything to help him! Sebastian, you are unkind!
That's nothin to do with us! Come along now.

*knew from seeing before

He thought I was Sebastian! He saved my brother from drowning . . . perhaps he is still alive!

A dishonest boy, not to help his friend. And a coward, too.
Yes, a coward, I believe it.

Then I'll go after him and fight him!
Let's go and see what happens.
I'll bet my money that nothing will.

Meanwhile, Feste the clown had been sent to find Cesario. Instead he came upon Sebastian.
You tell me that you are *not* Master Cesario . . . I was *not* sent by my lady to ask you to come to her?
You are a foolish fellow Go away!
Sir Andrew made the same mistake.
Are all these people crazy
Well, sir, we meet again!
There! What do you say to that?
I say there! And there! And there!

.et him
lone, sir!
)raw your
word!
I will!
I must tell Lady
Olivia of this at
once!

'hey began to
ight. But just
hen Lady Oli-
ia rushed in.
Stop, Toby! At once,
I say!
Madam!

our manners are
t for nothing but
e stable!* Get out
my sight!
How beau-
tiful she is!

en for animals

Dear Cesario, don't be angry! Come with me to the house.
Am I mad or dreaming? Well, if it's a dream, let me sleep on!
What? Are you willing to do what I say?
Yes,
cours
I will
Sebastian went into the palace with Olivia and talked with her for some time. Later, he walked in the garden.
I am not crazy, and neither is she! She's wonderful!
Antonio was not at the inn. If only I could find him, he might advise me.
Why worry? We are happy . . . an
here she comes!

My love, if you agree, this good priest will marry us right now.
en he will keep it cret until you wish ople to know of it. nat do you say?
Olivia and Sebastian were married even though Olivia still believed Sebastian was Cesario. Afterward, Sebastian went to look for Antonio.
I will do it. And having promised to be true to you, I always will be!
Vhile all this was appening, Duke rsino made up is mind to visit livia himself.
ood clown, go and tell our mistress I am here.
Yes, at once!

As the clown walked away, the duke's officers appeared with Antonio.
Here comes the man who kept Sir Andrew from fighting with me!
I remember his face. He was captain of a ship that sank one of my ships!
This is the man who sank the *Phoenix*. We caught him fighting in the streets here!
Whatever brought you here when you knew we were your enemies?
I wil tell you, sir.
It was that ungrate ful* boy by your side! I saved his lif cared for him, and came to this place to defend him.

*not showing proper thanks

Today, not willing to share my danger, he said he did not know me. And he refused me my own money I'd given him to use!
How can this be?
When did he come to this town?
Today, sir. But for the last three months we have been together all the time!
This cannot be! For three months this young man has been here with me!
Here comes Countess Olivia. Take this man aside for a moment.
Dear Countess!
What do you want?

Beautiful Olivia. . . .
There you are, Cesario! Where have you been?
The duke wishes to speak to you.
You are ungrateful and cruel! I could almost kill you!
Better yet, I will kill this boy whom you love! Come with me, Cesario!
Cesario! Where are you going? Someone—call the priest* that was here before!
I'm going with the duke—whom I love more than life.
Cesario! Dear husband, no!
Husband?

*a holy man, a minister

Yes, husband!
Her husband?
No, sir, not I.
Don't be afraid to say it, Cesario!

At that moment the priest walked in.
Father! Tell them what happened between this young man and me a short time ago.
I joined you together in the holy bonds of love and marriage.
Why, you ungrateful man!
Goodbye; the countess is yours. But see that you and I never meet again!
But I protest!*

*object to

Suddenly Sir Andrew arrived, all bloody.
Call a doctor, quick! And one for Sir Toby! He broke both our heads!
Who has done this, Sir Andrew?

The duke's gentleman, Cesario. And here he is!
You wanted to fight me, but I did not hurt you!

Here comes Sir Toby now. Doesn't he look hurt? Do you think he did it *himself*?
Get them to bed, and have their wounds* cared for.

*injuries, hurts

As if things were not confused enough, just then Sebastian appeared.
Dear Olivia, I'm sorry to have hurt your uncle and his friend. But I had to defend myself when they attacked me!
Impossible! There's one face, one voice, one look . . . but two people!
Sebastian, are you . . . *you*?
What's happening here?
Antonio! I've looked for you everywhere. Where have you been?
Sebastian! How can you be two people?
Do *I* stand there? Who is it? I never had a brother. My sister was drowned in the sea. . . .
My father was Sebastian . . . my brother, too . . . but *he* was drowned.

If you were a woman, I would weep tears of joy and say, "Welcome, Viola!"
If that is all you need, the welcome me!
So, dear wife, you have married both a maiden* and a man!
Boy, you have said a thousand times that you could never love a woman the way you love *me*!
And I'll say it again and again!
Now I believe it. Give me you hand. Let me see you in woman's clothes.
The captain who rescued me has them. Malvolio kno where he is.

*a young woman

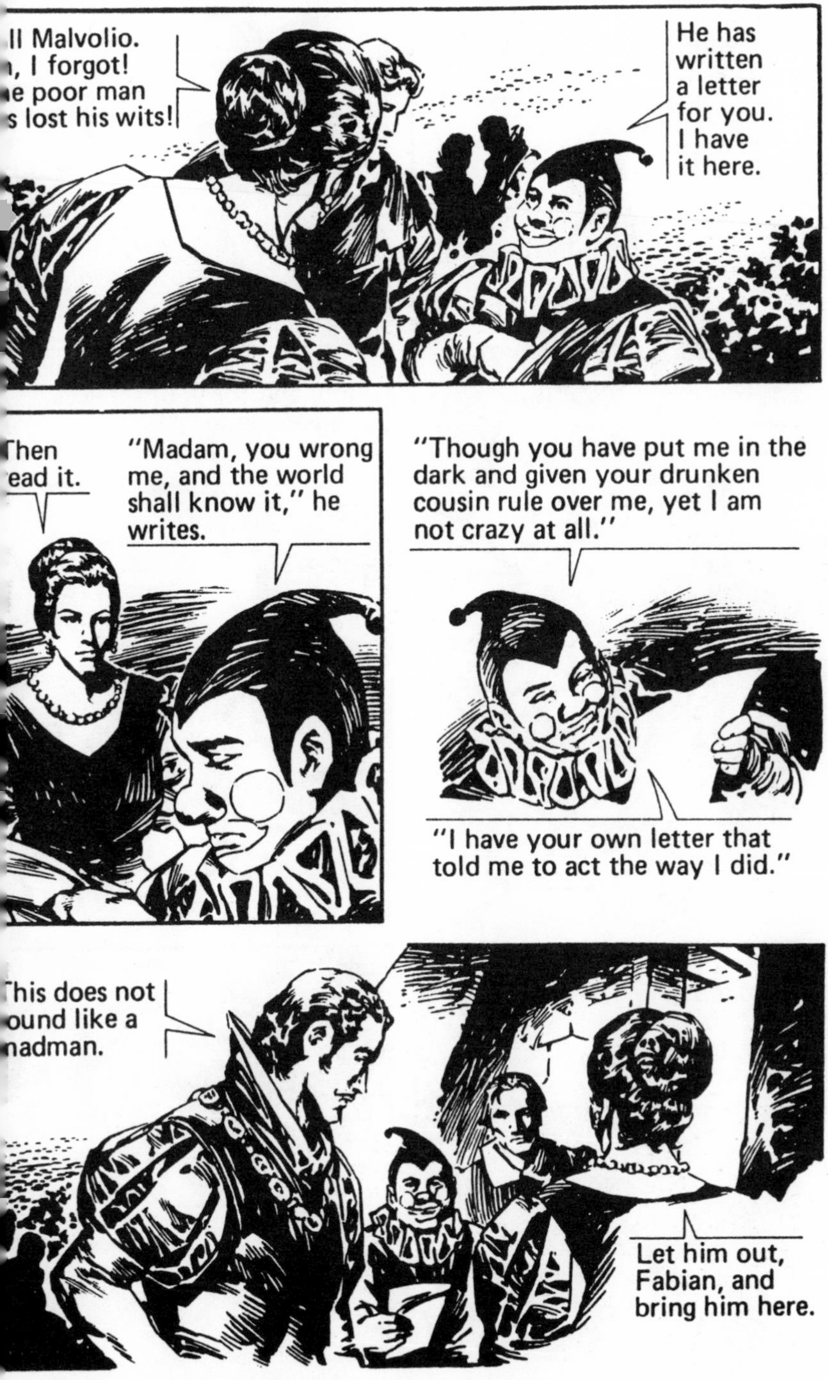
ll Malvolio.
ı, I forgot!
ıe poor man
s lost his wits!
He has written a letter for you. I have it here.
Then
ead it.
"Madam, you wrong me, and the world shall know it," he writes.
"Though you have put me in the dark and given your drunken cousin rule over me, yet I am not crazy at all."
"I have your own letter that told me to act the way I did."
This does not
ound like a
nadman.
Let him out, Fabian, and bring him here.

Meanwhile, sir, if you'll accept me as a sister-in-law* instead of a wife, your wedding will be held at my house.
Madam, I accept your offer!
I dismiss** you from your job; and for your services so well done . . .
. . . here is my hand! From no on you shall be my wife!
At that moment Malvolio rushed in.
Is this the madman?
Yes, it is.
Madam, here your letter! Everything I did was what you told me to do!

*one's brother's wife

**let go

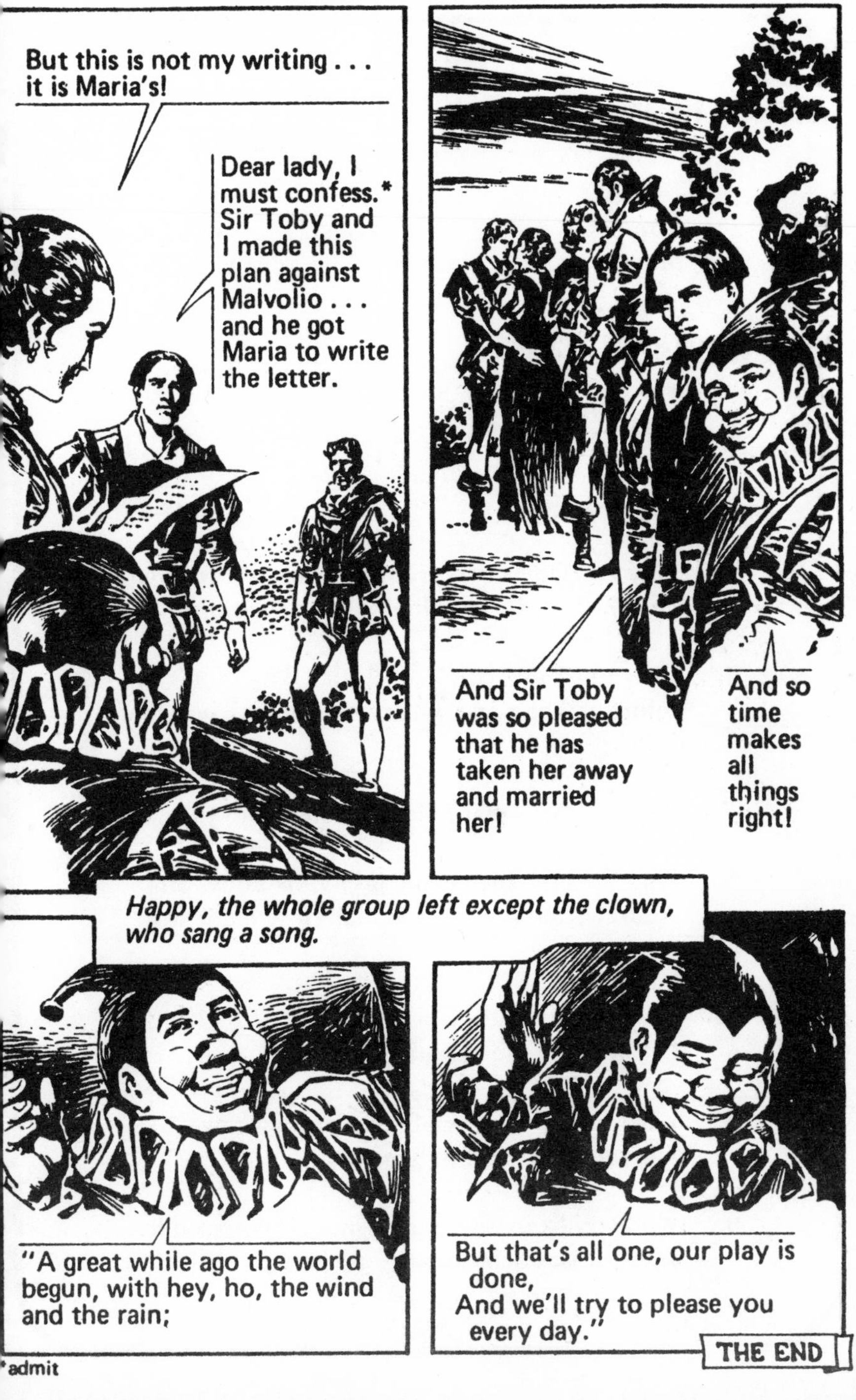
But this is not my writing . . . it is Maria's!
Dear lady, I must confess.* Sir Toby and I made this plan against Malvolio . . . and he got Maria to write the letter.
And Sir Toby was so pleased that he has taken her away and married her!
And so time makes all things right!
Happy, the whole group left except the clown, who sang a song.
"A great while ago the world begun, with hey, ho, the wind and the rain;
But that's all one, our play is done,
And we'll try to please you every day."
THE END

*admit

words to know

confused	faithful	court (verb)
stooping	recognized	untangle
protest	steward	ungrateful

questions

1. What task did Duke Orsino give Viola (Cesario)? As time went on, how did Viola begin to feel about the job?

2. Why had Olivia decided not to marry for seven years? What do you think of her decision?

3. How had Viola come to Illyria? Why didn't she return to her own country on the first available ship?

4. Who was Sebastian? How did he get to Illyria?

5. What was the plan made up by Sir Toby, Sir Andrew, and the maid Maria? How did it work out?

6. Why did Sir Andrew want to fight a duel with Cesario? Who interrupted the duel?

7. What happened when Sebastian first saw Olivia? Who did Olivia think he was?

8. Why was Antonio so angry with the person he thought was Sebastian?